D1551120

HUNCHBACK OF NOTRE DAME

VICTOR HUGO

Adapted by Dr. Marion Kimberly

GALLERY BOOKS
An Imprint of W. H. Smith Publishers Inc.
112 Madison Avenue
New York City 10016

This edition published 1991 by Gallery Books,
an imprint of W.H.Smith Publishers, Inc.,
112 Madison Avenue, New York, New York 10016

ISBN 0-8317-1465-4

Gallery Books are available for bulk purchase for sales
promotions and premium use. For details write or telephone
the Manager of Special Sales, W.H.Smith Publishers, Inc.,
112 Madison Avenue, New York, New York 10016. (212) 532-6600

Produced by Hawk Books Limited, London

Printed in Spain

Paris, January 6th 1482. Since time immemorial the feast of the Epiphany was celebrated with a miracle play at the Palace of Justice but the common people enjoyed their own festival of singing and dancing in the Square in front of the Cathedral of Notre Dame, known as the Feast of Fools.
Sacrilege! Profanity!
The Feast
Don't go gypsy girl, dance again for us!
Suddenly ...
Look, it's the new Fools' Pope for this year!
The ugliest man we could find!
Yes, it's Quasimodo, the bell ringer! The hunchback of Notre Dame! Ha! Ha!

He hates people laughing at him!
He can't hear! He's deaf as well as ugly!
He'll kill him! Let him go!

Here comes Claude Frollo, the Archdeacon, my old professor! What's he going to do?

Seeing the priest, Quasimodo's anger vanishes.

He's our Pope! Leave him alone!

Unexpectedly ...
The hunchback is defending the priest!

Amazing - he has him tamed!

That evening as Pierre Gringoire was walking through a dark alley ...
Guards! Help!

I'm coming! Guards! Guards!
One of the attackers slips off unseen ...

AAAGH!
Stop! Drop that woman!
Hold on!
What is your name!
I'm Captain Febo de Chateaupers. At your service, beautiful lady.
Later ...
I'd rather stay behind with her ...
Thank you Captain ...
When the bowmen had marched off with their prisoners...
What happened? Oh yes! The hunchback ... the gypsy girl ... and a dark figure who reminded me of someone ...
I'd better forget all about it and find somewhere to sleep.
Gringoire was the unfortunate author of the miracle play for that year and was now utterly ruined ...
He walked the deserted streets for some time ...
Alms! To buy bread.

Spare a coin sir, for God's sake!
Gringoire fled from the beggars, terrified
Suddenly he found himself in a well-lit Square ...
Where am I?
In the Court of Miracles!
We'll take you to our king.
Yes, let's go in.
The Court of Miracles was an inn, a thieves' meeting place ...
I am the King of the Court of Miracles. How did you get here ...?
I'm called Pierre Gringoire, King...
Enough! You will be hanged, unless ...
... Any woman here will take you for her husband.

Don't hang him! I'll marry him!
It's Esmeralda!

My children - for the next four years, you are man and wife!

Later in Esmeralda's humble house ...
Understand, I only married you to save your life.
I am grateful and we'll be good friends.

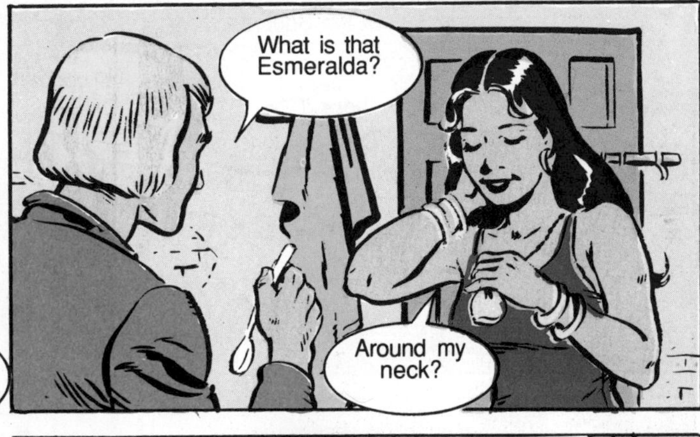
What is that Esmeralda?
Around my neck?

It's my lucky shoe and never leaves me.

A few days later in the Law Courts ...
You are accused of attempted kidnapping! Speak!
But Quasimodo, being deaf, can't hear what they ask him ...

Since you won't defend yourself, I shall pronounce sentence.

You will be flogged in the Square!

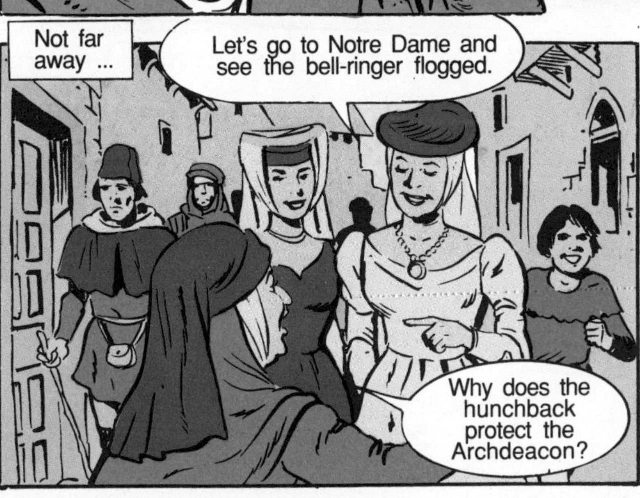
Not far away ...
Let's go to Notre Dame and see the bell-ringer flogged.
Why does the hunchback protect the Archdeacon?

Because the Archdeacon looked after him when he was a little boy.

The crowd arrives at the Square ...
Who is that mad looking woman?
She's not from around here.
No indeed!
Evil Gypsy girl! Out of my sight!
The gypsies stole her little girl when she was only a year old ...
She lives like a hermit in her tower, treasuring a little baby's shoe ...
And here comes the prisoner ...
Take off his shirt!
¡ZAS!
AAAGH!
Water ...
Water! Water!

Poor unfortunate ...

Here, drink ...

Don't touch me - you scare me!

Your fiancèe, Fleur, is very beautiful Febo.
Indeed!

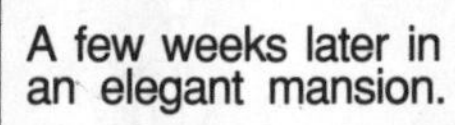
A few weeks later in an elegant mansion.

Come to the window - someone is singing in the Square.

You come too, Febo.

Esmeralda, with her goat Djali, is singing and dancing in the Square.

Who's that dark man staring at the dancer?
Look how he's watching her! It's Archdeacon Frollo!
And she's the gypsy girl whose life I saved.
She's the girl you told us about?
Tell her to come up and dance for us.
Hey! Gypsy girl!
Come up, little one!
Where are you going, Esmeralda?
What are you doing with the gypsy girl?
She's my wife - although she loves another man.
We've not seen each other for a long time, Gringoire. Tell me about the gypsy.
She saved my life by marrying me but she's in love with someone called Febo.

Meanwhile ...
You're more beautiful than I remembered but you don't remember me?
Oh yes! I know you!
Why do you two get on so well?
What has the goat got round his neck?
That's my secret
Oh!
Take no notice of them!
Quick, look what the goat's spelled out!
She's a witch!
Out of here, cursed gypsy girl!
Hey, wait!

Wait, little one!
What do you want?
That afternoon in the Archdeacon's cell, his brother Jean bursts in.
I can't concentrate - can't think of anything but what Gringoire told me ...
I wonder what's wrong with my virtuous brother ...
Why are you here?
I want to ask you a favour ...
Money, as always!
I need it for food ...
For drink, you mean!
I swear by all that's holy, that's not true!

Don't blaspheme! Here you are!
Thank you dear brother!
Jean leaves, pleased, but the priest follows him ...
Well let's go and drink this money I got from my dear brother!
Okay, but later I've got a date with a gypsy girl.
Hi Febo! Where have you been?
To visit my fiancée.
It must be the same Febo ...
A few hours later ...
Let's have a drink in here ...
I've got to go Jean, I'll be late for my date ...

Wake up man! Give me some money!

Febo goes off - leaving his friend asleep in the doorway.

Sorry brother but I have to go after him ...

Someone's following me.

I have nothing of value on me!

You're Captain Febo, aren't you?
How do you know my name?

I know you've got a date with a gypsy girl too, what's her name?
Esmeralda.

You lie!
You insult me! Draw your sword!

You've forgotten your date.

We shall meet again but first, your appointment ...
If you give me money ...

Take it - but show me you're not lying!
I'll take you with me ... hide you ...

Has the gypsy girl arrived?
Not yet, but come in ...

Follow me.

Okay, you can go now.

Hide here. I'll be back with the girl.
Okay.

A few minutes later ...
Come in little one. Here we can talk undisturbed.
Yes, it's her.
Do you love me?
More than anything in the world.
Swear to me you've never loved another.
I swear it!
Suddenly.
AAAH!
The mysterious figure stabs Febo and escapes ...
through the window ...

Moments later, as Esmeralda revives ...
What happened?
She's a witch! She's murdered the Captain!
Arrest her!
Let's go. You'll be hanged for this.
A month later, Gringoire is passing the Law Courts ...
What's going on?
They're trying a witch who killed a Captain of the Guard.
Let's go in and see ...
Where is the accused?
Can't see - the crowd's hiding her.
You are accused of having stabbed Captain Febo ...
I'm innocent I never stabbed anyone.
Oh Febo, how cruel fate has been to us.

For pity's sake, is the Captain dead?
He is dying ...

I'm innocent but my life doesn't matter if Febo dies.
All the evidence shows you're guilty. You will hang.

It was that terrible man in black. I'm innocent, Febo.
Poor Esmeralda.

A few days later ...
Who are you?
A priest.

Tomorrow you die. Are you prepared?
Yes.

I'm cold. I want to get out of here.
Come with me then.

I know you! You are the murderer of my Febo! Go! You disgust me!
You hate me so much!

Yes, I hate you!
It hurts me to hear this ...

Out of here, devil!
I could save you - come with me.

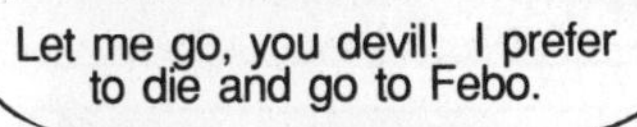
Let me go, you devil! I prefer to die and go to Febo.

Don't speak that name!

The day of the execution outside Notre Dame.

Go monstrous assassin and let me die in peace!

Today we're going to see a gypsy die, old woman.
What's her name?

Esmeralda! Soon she'll hang from the gallows!
Wonderful! I hate that gypsy girl ...

Meanwhile at Fleur's house ...
Where have you been all this time Febo?
Wounded.
Oh my dear! Tell me ...
Don't worry, it was nothing, I'm fine.
I am worried, tell me!
A silly fight over nothing.
Over what?
A horse - it's all over now.
I think it's a witch who's going to be hanged.
What has that girl done? Who is she?
I don't know. Let's see.
At that moment.
To the gallows!
Die, accursed gypsy!
HA! HA! HA!

Yes! It's that terrible gypsy girl.
What gypsy girl?
Don't you remember? What's the matter?
Nothing ...
This girl seems to worry you.
Don't be silly - come inside.
Let's stay and watch.
That horrid priest again!
Go away, you devil!
Woman, have you begged forgiveness for your sins!
I can still save you ...
What's happened to my beloved Febo?

He's dead.
Then I want to die too.
Well die then!
Oh, what do I see? A hallucination?
Febo I'm innocent! Why are you leaving?
Febo, Febo, are you really alive?
The hangman is about to place the noose around Esmeralda's neck ...
Suddenly
AAAY!

OUF!
CLOCK!
Bravo! Bravo!

Sanctuary!

Sanctuary!
Look how he climbs the rope!

Later in a little room in Notre Dame
Why did you save me?

In the meantime ...
Dead! She may already be dead! It's my fault.

But I prefer that to her hatred.

After a few hours of wandering around, the Archdeacon returns to the Cathedral.

She'll haunt me till I die!

The ghost of Esmeralda!

I know my ugliness frightens you, so don't look at me, just listen ...

Stay here during the day-time. At night you can walk in the church.
But never leave the Cathedral. The Law grants immunity to those who take refuge in Notre Dame.

If you leave you'll be killed and I'll die of unhappiness.

Why did you rescue me?

Wait! Don't go!

Did you call? I'm deaf, I can't hear.

But if you speak slowly I can lip-read.

Why did you save me?
Because you were kind to me once. I must go now.

I nearly forgot. Blow this whistle if you need me. It's the only thing I can hear.
That night.
Go, devil! Help! Help!
Oh! The priest! Help!
Wait - don't be afraid ...
I only want to talk - calm yourself.
Suddenly Esmeralda remembers the whistle ...
What's that?
Quasimodo!
02058
24

But in the darkness Quasimodo can't see who it is ...
How can I show him it's me? He can't hear ...
I'll take him outside so he won't frighten you any more ...
Fortunately for the priest the moon shone strongly ...
You?

Monseigneur! Punish me!

A few days later, at the Court of Miracles ...
Esmeralda's taken sanctuary in Notre Dame ...

And they say the Law will get her and hang her ...
We must save her!

Yes! To the rescue of Esmeralda!
Esmeralda!

Meanwhile, from her prison, Esmeralda has seen someone

Febo, is it really you? You must hear me ... Febo!

That's his horse. I'll wait.

Esmeralda turns to her only friend ...
I must speak to him. Please find him.

Some hours later ...
Ah, Captain - there's someone wants to talk to you!
Listen! It's Esmeralda, she's waiting ...
Do you come from the other world?

Tell her she can wait then! I'm going to get married!

And the Captain takes off ...
The following night, at the Court of Miracles ...
We'll show them tonight!
To Esmeralda's rescue!
It's midnight - we must cross Paris in silence.
Come on!
It's locked! Break in!
We're here, light your torches!
We're ready!
I can't force it!
Keep trying! It'll give way ...
Suddenly, out of the sky ...
¡AAGH!

It came from nowhere! Witchcraft!
From the top of the tower Quasimodo had seen the rescuers and was, as he thought, protecting Esmeralda.
They shan't take her!
But the beggars hadn't seen Quasimodo ...
You're scared of a beam?
He's right, we can use it to break down the door!
TORRE GROSA
Ready lads!
Rocks falling from the sky!
I've got an idea. Wait here.
A few minutes later ...
This ladder will get us into the Cathedral!

Quick!
I'll not let you harm her!
AAAGH!
Meanwhile in Esmeralda's cell ...
Come quickly! My friend will get you out of this!
Here he is!
Oh, not you!
That's how you repay me for saving you?
I'd rather die than be anywhere near you!
The old woman will guard you while I fetch the soldiers.

Don't let her escape, if you want to see her hanged!
She won't escape ...

Why do you hate me so much?
Because one of your people stole my baby.

Look - when I find the twin to this I'll find my child.

They match!
My daughter!
My daughter! I've found you at last! But you must flee ...
Goodbye Mother - we'll see each other again!
We've got you!
Just then ...
They've taken her! How?
It was the Archdeacon.
It's all his fault!
I hate you! I hate you!
And the Arch-deacon is thrown from the tower ...
Esmeralda! They're going to hang her ...
And poor Esmeralda died still in love with the treacherous Captain, and not knowing that the hunchback had loved her with a truly unselfish love.
The End